PUFFIN BOOKS

PONDER AND WILLIAM

Ponder's everyday job was to take care of William's pyjamas. But
when William was staying with Cousin Winifred for weekends he
did all sorts of other things as well. Like going flying with a kite, or
painting himself as well as the garden seat, or being chased by a
hedgehog (which he thought was a scrubbing brush), or falling into
his own currant cake, or digging up all the lettuce seeds because he
thought William had put them in upside down.

But Ponder wanted to be good, and William, who always *was* good,
helped him as much as he could, and at the end of each gay and happy
day Ponder made up a song to celebrate it.

This is a book to be read aloud to the very young, and after they have
shared Ponder's special discoveries in the Summer, Autumn, Winter,
and Spring, they will be able to tell their own day's adventures and
perhaps even make up songs about them as Ponder does. Most of
Ponder's songs can be sung to well-known nursery rhymes and other
tunes. We have suggested which ones. One or two may need an extra
note put in, a word left out, or a line sung twice, but they are great
fun to try to sing.

Barbara Softly

Ponder and William

With drawings by Diana John

PUFFIN BOOKS

Puffin Books, Penguin Books Ltd, Harmondsworth, Middlesex, England
Penguin Books, 625 Madison Avenue, New York, New York 10022, U.S.A.
Penguin Books Australia Ltd, Ringwood, Victoria, Australia
Penguin Books Canada Ltd, 2801 John Street, Markham, Ontario, Canada L3R 1B4
Penguin Books (N.Z.) Ltd, 182–190 Wairau Road, Auckland 10, New Zealand

First published 1966
Reprinted 1967, 1970, 1972, 1973, 1974, 1975, 1977, 1981

Made and printed in Great Britain by
Hazell Watson & Viney Ltd,
Aylesbury, Bucks
Set in Monotype Bembo

Contents

Introduction

Ponder and William

William was four years old and he lived in the town, which was full of red buses, cars, and bicycles. There was only the Park where he could go out to play. But, once in the summer, once in the autumn, once in the winter, and once in the spring, he was allowed to spend two whole days all by himself with Cousin Winifred in the country.

Cousin Winifred lived in a little house, in a little lane which went down to a road where green buses ran into a village and ducks swam on a pond. Cousin Winifred had a garden and all round her garden there were other people's gardens; there was a big apple tree; there was a vegetable patch; there were flower-beds; there was grass. Cousin Winifred had three cats – Tigger, who was striped like a tiger; Ginnie, who was small and black and white; and Marmalade, who was the same colour as his name, a lovely orange-gold. But, best of all, Cousin Winifred had Ponder the pyjama case, who sat on the spare-room bed and waited for the time to pass until William would come and stuff him with his pyjamas.

> 'Sing a song of summer-time,
> A pocket full of apples,'

sang Ponder, bouncing up and down with excitement

because this was the weekend that William was coming to stay.

What kind of a pyjama case do you think Ponder was? He wasn't a dog pyjama case, or a cat pyjama case, or even a lion pyjama case; he wasn't a teddy-bear or a duck or an elephant, or a giraffe or a hippopotamus, or a penguin or a tiger. He had little round ears, like a teddy-bear's, four stubby black legs, two black patches round his eyes, and a black band round his chest – and the rest of him was white. Do you know what he was? He was a panda pyjama case.

> 'Sing a song of summer-time,
> A pocket full of apples,'

sang Ponder again, and this time, this time when he bounced on the bed, the door flew open and there

stood William with his weekend suitcase in his hand.

William smiled and smiled and Ponder stared back at him, his dark eyes shining and bright. And then – and then he winked at William, a very long, slow wink as if he found it hard to keep one eye open and the other one shut.

'Ha – llo, William,' said Ponder in a very gruff voice.

William smiled and smiled and then he dropped his weekend suitcase on the floor, scrambled on to the bed, seized Ponder's stubby, black paws, and laughed and laughed.

'Ha – llo, Ponder,' he said.

Ponder and William laughed so much and rolled on the bed for so long that Cousin Winifred called up

the stairs to say that there wouldn't be any tea if the eiderdown wasn't pulled straight and William's suitcase wasn't unpacked by the time she had counted up to twenty.

So Ponder sat still and tried to look good. William smoothed the eiderdown and unpacked his weekend suitcase. He put his shoes and slippers on the floor, his pants, shirts, socks, and vest in the drawers, his tooth-brush in the mug on the window-sill and – where do you think he put his pyjamas? Yes, he tucked them inside Ponder. Ponder looked fat and firm and very pleased with himself.

'Now we'll go and have some tea,' said William. 'But you must remember to say "please" and "thank you" and eat up your bread and butter before you ask for cake.'

'I like bread and butter,' said Ponder, 'and I like cake.'

He jumped off the bed and scampered to the door.

'Sing a song of summer-time,
A pocket full of apples,'

he chanted.

William ran after him and they hurried down the stairs together paw in hand.

Ponder's Song of the Cats

(Tune – *Oh where, oh where, has my
little dog gone?*)

Tigger and Ginnie and Marmalade
Are cats in the garden at home.
During the day, they will sometimes play,
But at night they like to roam.

Tigger and Ginnie and Marmalade
Go out when I'm sent up to bed,
Out in the night in the moonlight bright
While the stars shine overhead.

Tigger and Ginnie and Marmalade
Will dance with the moths on the wall,
Chase in the grass the shadows which pass
And climb up the chimneys tall.

Tigger and Ginnie and Marmalade
Come home with the sun in the dawn.
Twelve muddy paws creep softly indoors
And three heads wearily yawn.

Tigger and Ginnie and Marmalade
Would lie in their baskets all day.
But up in the tree - what can they see?
Me - so they come out to play.

Ponder at the Seaside

After tea Ponder and William went into the garden to find the three cats, Tigger, Ginnie, and Marmalade. Tigger, Ginnie, and Marmalade were sitting in the middle of the grass waiting for the moths to start flying when the sun had gone down behind the apple tree. The sky was already turning pink and red and gold.

'It's going to be a fine day tomorrow,' said Ponder, 'and we shall be able to go out.'

'Where?' asked William.

Ponder did not know exactly where, but he said it might be to watch the green buses on the road at the bottom of the lane, or it might be to feed the ducks on the pond in the village, or it might be to go shopping for Cousin Winifred and buy sugar, butter, and tea.

Ponder was right. In the morning the sun was shining, the sky was blue, and Cousin Winifred said she would take them both out. But it wasn't to watch the green buses, or to feed the ducks, or to go shopping. Cousin Winifred said she would take them to the seaside.

Ponder had never been to the seaside before and all the way to catch the train – down the lane, into the village, past the pond, and on to the station – he kept asking questions about it. William said there was sand and lots and lots of water.

'More water than there is in the birdbath in the garden?' asked Ponder.

'Much more,' said William.

'More than in the bath in the bathroom?' asked Ponder.

'Much more,' said William.

'More than in the pond in the village?'

'Much, much more,' said William.

Ponder was silent after that. He could not imagine anything with more water in it than the pond in the village.

At the station he stood holding William's hand until they heard the train coming – *whoo-oo-oo* it whistled and made everybody jump. In the train Ponder sat on William's knee and looked out of the window to watch the trees and houses and cows rushing by. Sometimes the train stopped at another station; sometimes it whistled – *whoo-oo-oo* to let everyone know that it was coming and then it did not stop, but went clacketty-clacketty-clack past all the people waiting on the platform.

As soon as they reached the seaside William bought Ponder a little bucket and spade so that he could dig in the sand. Then they went down to the shore together.

Ponder stood and stared and stared at the water. He had never seen anything so enormous before. It went as far as he could see until it touched the sky, blue and shining in the sun. Ponder wriggled his toes in the warm sand.

'I like the seaside,' he said.

'Let's make a sandcastle,' said William.

Ponder put down his bucket and began to dig. First they piled up a great mound of sand, patted and smoothed its sides with their spades and stuck it with shells for windows and doors. Then they filled their buckets with sand and made a ring of small castles all round the big one; and then they built a wall right round the big castle and the little castles.

'I'm going to find some stones to put on top of the wall,' said William and he raced away up the beach to where Cousin Winifred was sitting on the shingle.

Ponder stayed by the castle. He was sure it was the best castle that had ever been built. He patted it with his spade and he put trails of green seaweed round each of the tiny castles, to look like grass. Suddenly – he heard a noise, a soft, swishing noise and there was the sea sending a little wave right up to the castle wall.

'Go away, sea,' said Ponder.

And the sea went away. The little wave slid down the beach and disappeared. But there was another wave behind and it came tumbling up the shore towards Ponder and the castle.

'Away, sea, away!' Ponder cried, whirling his wooden spade round and round his head.

'Awa-ay!' he shouted. He chased the wave down the beach and stood there looking very fierce indeed.

Out on the water Ponder could see another wave, bigger and stronger than the first two. It came rolling towards him, green, blue, sparkling in the sun, and there were little flecks of white scurrying along with it.

'Awa-ay!' Ponder began.

But the wave didn't take any notice. It came rolling up the beach as fast as it could.

Ponder walked backwards, whirling his wooden spade, and just when the wave was nearly touching his toes – Ponder tripped over, over the wall of the castle and over the ring of little castles. He sat down, bump, right on top of the big castle in the middle. The wave came too, over the wall, over the little castles – and then it stopped, splashing and dancing all round; and there was Ponder, safe and dry, whirling

his wooden spade, laughing and shouting, 'Awa-ay, sea, awa-ay!'

When William saw Ponder sitting on top of the big castle with sea all round him, he came running down the beach.

'Come out, Ponder!' he shouted. 'You'll get wet.'

Ponder waved his wooden spade over the side of the castle and dipped it in the water.

'I'm in a boat!' he cried. 'This is fun, William, I'm rowing a boat.'

William dropped his spade and the stones he had found and he paddled through the water to Ponder's side. He lifted Ponder off the castle and set him on the dry sand.

'The next wave might be even bigger still,' he said. 'I think we'd better build another castle higher up.'

'I'd rather build a boat,' said Ponder. 'We could sit in it and have our dinner.'

So Ponder and William built a boat with seats to sit on and a wheel to steer it; and while they were eating their dinner they watched all the other boats out on the sea. Some had sails and were blown along by the wind; some had tall funnels and went fast;

some were paddled slowly along beside the shore, and some were bright, red motor-boats which went chug-chug-chug over the smooth, blue waves and sent the white spray flying.

'I like those best,' said Ponder. 'Our boat is a motor-boat.'

At last, when it was time to go home, Ponder held his bucket in one paw, his spade in the other. He waved to the boat they had made of sand and to the boats on the sea.

'Good-bye, seaside,' he said. 'I hope we come again another day.'

And William hoped so, too.

Ponder's Song of the Boats

If I had a boat
With sails and mast,
The winds would blow
To make us go
Away on the waves
That roll so fast.

If I had a boat
With funnels tall,
Engines to pound
Propellers round,
The winds would not have
To blow at all.

If I had a boat
With one brown oar;
A wind that's light,
A sea that's slight,
I'd paddle it there
Beside the shore.

But I want a boat
To ride the sea,
To cleave a way
Of foaming spray -
And the motor-boat's
The boat for me!

Ponder Feeds the Ducks

Ponder and William woke up too late the next morning to do anything except play in the garden until dinner-time. They pretended that the grass was the sea and they were the bright red motor-boats going chug-chug-chug over the smooth, green lawn. Sometimes Tigger, Ginnie, and Marmalade came bounding towards them and then the cats had to be the sailing-boats that were blown along by the wind.

After dinner William said they were going to the village to feed the ducks on the pond.

'Feed the ducks!' said Ponder and his eyes grew round with excitement. 'Whoo-oo-oo,' he went like the train in the station and he scampered into the kitchen to find some bread.

When he opened the bread bin, he saw four slices of a brown loaf and one thick piece of currant cake.

'Do ducks like currants?' he asked.

'They might,' said William, and he put the bread and cake into a paper bag.

Ponder held the paper bag tightly in one paw and held William's hand in the other as they went down the lane to the main road. At the bottom of the lane Ponder began to be quite impatient when he had to wait on the pavement for all the cars, buses, and bicycles to go by.

'Hurry up, cars,' he said.

'Look both ways, and both ways again, and if there is nothing coming we can run across,' said William.

As soon as Ponder was on the other side of the road, he ran as fast as he could into the village so that he would be the first to see the ducks. He turned the

corner and there was the pond, golden in the sun, with the trees bending down looking at themselves in the water.

'Tea-time, ducks, tea-time,' Ponder called.

He climbed on to the wooden railing and leaned over the bar.

'Bread first and cake afterwards,' he said, bouncing up and down.

When the ducks heard Ponder they began to swim and fly towards him until the pond and sky seemed full of them.

'Quack-quack-quack,' they said to each other.

When Ponder began to crumble the bread in his paws – 'Gub-gub-gub,' they said, making sloshy noises in the water with their bills.

Ponder crumbled the bread carefully and tried to throw it so that even the slowest duck would have something to eat. At last, his paw reached the bottom of the bag and he pulled out the piece of cake. It was nearly black with currants.

'Supposing,' said Ponder to William, 'supposing the currants drop to the bottom of the pond and the ducks can't find them. What a waste of fat, juicy currants!' Ponder was very fond of currants.

'Throw the cake in and see what the ducks do,' said William.

Ponder crumbled the cake into tiny pieces.

'Whoo-oosh!' he said and showered it all at once over the excited ducks.

Suddenly, every duck on the pond seemed to be

standing on its head – not a bill or a beady eye was to
be seen. They were busy underneath the water suck-
ing up the fat, juicy currants. Ponder and William had
never seen anything so funny as all the brown tails
sticking up in the air. They laughed so much that the
paper bag fell out of Ponder's paw into the water.

'Quack-quack-quack,' said the ducks. They stopped
eating currant cake and tried to eat paper bag instead.

First Ponder tried to reach the paper bag and then
William tried, but the ducks kept pushing it farther
and farther away.

'We want a stick,' Ponder cried and he ran down
to the trees to pick up a long branch with twiggy
pieces on the end of it.

'It's just like a fishing-rod,' said William.

William held the stick, Ponder held the end of William's shirt so that he would not tumble into the water, and William stretched his arm – out – out – over the pond and hooked up the paper bag.

'Quack-quack-quack,' went the ducks as the paper bag sailed into the air, and they seemed to be saying, 'We like currant cake and we like paper bag!'

'Greedy ducks,' said Ponder. 'You've had your tea and now we're going home to ours.'

William squeezed the paper bag and pushed it in his pocket.

'Good-bye, ducks,' he said.

The ducks swam happily away. Some stood on the banks to clean their feathers; some poked among the weeds and some tucked their heads under their wings and went to sleep. The pond was quiet again, golden in the sun, with the trees bending down looking at themselves in the water.

'Good-bye, ducks,' said Ponder.

'Qua-ack, qua-a-ack,' was the sleepy reply.

Ponder's Song of the Ducks

Down on the pond there are hundreds of
   ducks,
Hundreds and hundreds and hundreds of
   ducks.

Ducks on the shore seem to bask in the sun,
Smoothing and stroking their feathers, each
   one.
Some tuck their brown heads right under
   their wings,
Sleeping and dreaming of wonderful things –
Sloshy, wet mudbanks, all shady and black,
Ducklings that call to them – quack, quack,
   quack.

Ducks on the water happily gliding
Sail as small boats on a calm sea riding;
Some in a whirlwind of flap and flurry,
Feet paddling fast in a foam of hurry,
Fluttering feathers and eyes shiny black,
Poke out their necks crying – quack, quack,
   quack.

Whatever they're doing, wherever they are,
When I'm at the railings they come from
  afar;
Flying and swimming and running to see
What's in the parcel I've brought for their
  tea.
Whether it's breadcrumbs or currants so
  black,
Thank you, they say to me – quack, quack,
  quack.

Down on the pond there are hundreds of
  ducks,
Hundreds and hundreds and hundreds of
  ducks.

Ponder and the Apple Tree

That evening William and Cousin Winifred were busy in the bedroom and Ponder was sitting on the window-sill so that he would not be in the way. Ponder was tired of sitting still and he was wondering what he could do. He looked out of the window and there, at the end of the garden was the apple tree. On all its branches there were apples, green ones, yellow-green ones, and ripe, red ones – and the ripe, red ones were right at the top.

'I should like to pick one of those ripe, red apples and eat it,' said Ponder to himself. 'I wonder what William would say?'

But he did not wait to ask William what he would say. As soon as William and Cousin Winifred went into the bathroom to put some blankets in the airing cupboard, Ponder hopped off the window-sill and scampered across the landing. At the top of the stairs he looked back round the corner to see if William was coming after him – but he wasn't.

Ponder ran down the stairs and into the kitchen. The window was open because Tigger, Ginnie, and Marmalade liked to go in and out by themselves. Underneath the window was the sink. Ponder put his four paws together and made one big jump – whoo-oo-oop the sink was slippery and Ponder nearly fell in. He reached the window safely and then turned round again to see if William was coming – but he wasn't. Ponder scrambled through the window down into the garden.

The garden looked very large to him at first. There were rows of flowers on one side and grass on the other. In the middle was a winding path. Ponder thought it best to walk on the path in case he got his feet wet. Up the path he went, up some steps and into the vegetable garden where there were rows of cabbages and carrots. At the top of the steps Ponder turned round – to see if William was coming – but he wasn't.

Ponder went on, through the cabbages and carrots and on to the grass under the apple tree. One of the cats, Tigger, was sitting there washing his face; on the wall near the apple tree Ginnie was pretending to be asleep and on the lowest branch of the apple tree, Marmalade was swaying up and down.

'Hallo, cats,' said Ponder. 'I'm going to climb that tree and pick one of those ripe, red apples to eat.'

Tigger, Ginnie, and Marmalade said nothing. They just sat and watched. Ponder ran to the foot of the tree, and then he peered round the trunk – to see if William was coming – but he wasn't.

Ponder dug his claws into the tree-trunk and began to climb upwards up – up – up, past the branch where Marmalade was perched, past all the green apples hiding in the shade – and then he peered through the leaves to the house to see if William was coming – but he wasn't. On Ponder went, past the yellow-green apples until he seemed to be right at the top of the tree and on every branch there were the ripe, red apples that he wanted to eat. When he couldn't climb any farther, Ponder sat still. He could see over the fence into the garden next door, and over that fence into another garden, and over that to roofs and chimneys, fields and more trees.

'Cats,' Ponder called out, 'I can see the whole world from up here, I'm sure.'

Tigger, Ginnie, and Marmalade said nothing, but they all turned round and looked up the garden – to see if William was coming – but he wasn't.

Ponder wriggled, clung on to the tree with three paws, stretched out the fourth paw and pulled off his ripe, red apple.

'There, I've picked my apple,' he shouted, and he stuffed it in his mouth because it would be much easier to climb down if he had all his paws free.

Then Ponder looked up the garden towards the house, and Tigger, Ginnie, and Marmalade looked up the garden towards the house – to see if William was coming – AND HE WAS!

Ponder was so surprised that he let go of the apple tree and fell, down, down, through the leaves on to the very branch where Marmalade was perched. Marmalade was surprised, too, and he nearly fell off,

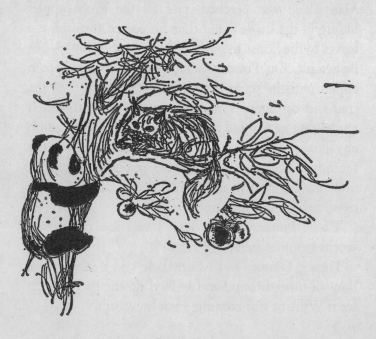

and the apple branch went up and down, up and down with Ponder and Marmalade clinging on to it topsy-turvy. When the branch had stopped going up and down, they both pulled themselves the right way up and Ponder ran along to the apple-trunk, dug in his claws, and slid bump-bump-bump to the grass at the bottom. Then he looked to see if William was still coming – and he was.

Ponder scampered into the vegetable patch and tried to hide behind a cabbage.

'Ponder,' called William. 'What are you doing behind that cabbage?'

Ponder took his apple out of his mouth.

'Looking for caterpillars,' he said.

'You've picked a ripe, red apple,' said William.

'I like apples,' said Ponder.

'You've climbed the apple tree,' said William, 'and you might have fallen out.' But he didn't sound at all cross.

'I hung on with all my claws,' said Ponder. 'It's people who haven't got claws who shouldn't try to climb apple trees.'

'I haven't got claws,' said William as they went indoors together. 'Now come and watch me pack my suitcase. It's nearly time for me to go home.'

'Home?' said Ponder. 'Already?' And he looked quite sad.

'But I'm coming back in the autumn.'

'When's autumn?'

'When the wind blows and all the leaves fall off the trees.'

Ponder smiled and his eyes shone.

'I like summer,' he said, 'but I shall like autumn even better.'

So Ponder sat on the bed and ate his apple while William put his clothes – shoes and slippers, pants, shirts, socks, and vest into his weekend suitcase – but he didn't pack his pyjamas.

'You can keep those, Ponder,' he said. 'I've plenty more at home and I'll bring another pair back with me when I come next time.'

Ponder looked fat and firm and very pleased with

himself and when William ran out of the room to go to the station with Cousin Winifred, he jumped off the bed on to the window-sill.

'Good-bye, William,' he shouted. 'See you in the autumn.'

He waved and waved until William was out of sight behind the trees in the lane.

Ponder's Song of the Apple Tree

Green apples, red apples,
Yellow – and brown
Where the wind bruised them
And tumbled them down.

Red apples, brown apples,
Yellow – and green,
Where the leaves hide them
No sun can be seen.

Yellow and brown apples,
Green ones – and red,
Red as the sun when
It sinks into bed.

Green apples, red apples,
Yellow as leaves,
Blown by the wind from
The gold autumn trees.

Yellow and brown apples,
Large apples, small;
Green apples – red ones,
The ripest of all.

Ponder and the Autumn Leaves

On the first morning after William came back again in the autumn, Ponder was looking out of the kitchen window and it seemed that the whole world had been turned into gold. There were golden marigolds along the edge of the path and golden sunflowers against the fence, and showers of golden leaves were flying from all the trees and being tossed up in the bright blue sky. Ponder scrambled through the window on to the path.

'Catch us, catch us!' cried the leaves as they whirled over his head.

Ponder ran up and down waving his paws, jumping after the leaves, but he could not catch any of them. He ran up the steps, through the vegetable garden and under the apple tree. He pulled down a branch and shook it hard. Showers of gold tumbled about him and were whirled away by the wind.

'Look, leaves,' Ponder shouted, 'I'm the wind, too. I can blow you up in the air. Whoo-oo-oo,' he puffed as the leaves danced over the fence.

On the fence the three cats, Tigger, Ginnie, and Marmalade were sitting. Their big, round eyes followed the leaves across the gardens until they were out of sight.

Then Ponder saw the broom propped against the

toolshed. He picked it up and began to sweep the path.

Brush – brush – brush went the broom and made the leaves dance more quickly than ever. Tigger, Ginnie, and Marmalade slid down the fence and leapt after the leaves – one – two – three.

'Ha, ha,' Ponder laughed. 'Can you catch my leaves, cats?'

And the cats could. Tigger jumped high in the air and caught his between his front paws; Ginnie rolled on her back clutching a leaf to her chest and Marmalade just sat on his leaf and looked as though he were saying – 'Now you can't fly away.'

Ponder swept the rest of the leaves into a big pile. 'Watch me, cats,' he called. 'I really am the wind.'

He bent down and caught up a huge armful of the gleaming gold.

'Whoosh!' he said, throwing it up into the air. 'Whoosh – whoosh – whoosh!'

The three cats and Ponder disappeared under the heap of gold as it came showering down.

'It's raining leaves,' Ponder shouted and he, Tigger and Ginnie and Marmalade had to wipe the leaves from their fur like raindrops on a wet day.

'Ponder,' called William from the kitchen window. 'It is dinner-time. Sweep up the leaves and then come in.'

Ponder worked hard once more pushing the scattered gold into a heap under the apple tree.

'There,' he puffed, because he was out of breath. 'Now I can eat my dinner.'

He went indoors and the three cats followed him.

All the time Ponder and William were eating their dinner, they could see the gold under the apple tree gleaming in the sun, and more leaves being whirled from the sky until the path, too, seemed paved with gold.

'I like leaves,' said Ponder happily. 'And I like playing at being the wind. Don't you?' he asked the three cats.

But Tigger, Ginnie, and Marmalade were fast asleep in their baskets.

'This afternoon,' said William, 'if the wind is still blowing, we can go up on the Common and fly my kite.'

Ponder looked puzzled.

'What's a kite?' he asked.

William laughed. 'Mine is red and it looks like a great red leaf with a long, long tail – and there's a piece of string tied on to the leaf part – and – and you hold the string and the leaf part and the tail go flying away in the sky all the time the wind is blowing – and – and they go on flying as far as the string will let them – and – and –' But William was out of breath and he couldn't say any more.

'Whoo-oo-oosh!' said Ponder excitedly. 'May I hold the string that is tied on to the leaf part?'

'Yes,' said William. 'If you promise not to let go.'

Ponder promised and he looked very pleased with himself indeed.

'I think I shall like flying a kite,' he said.

Ponder's Song of the Autumn Gold
(Tune – *Bobby Shaftoe*)

I took the broom and I swept the grass,
Brush and brush,
Brush and brush.
The cats jumped down when they saw me
    pass,
Brush and brush,
Brush.

The wind came too, and it blew us all,
Rush and rush,
Rush and rush,
On with the gold to the garden wall,
Rush and rush,
Rush.

We gathered the gold and packed it high,
Crush and crush,
Crush and crush,
And more came tumbling out of the sky,
Crush and crush,
Crush.

Under the tree – it mustn't be told,
Hush and hush,
Hush and hush,
We've hidden our store of autumn gold,
Hush, oh, hush,
Hush.

Ponder Flies a Kite

The wind was still blowing in the afternoon. In fact, it seemed to be blowing harder than ever. Cousin Winifred packed a picnic tea and Ponder and William raced in front to climb the hill to the Common.

First they ran, then they trotted, and then they had to walk, paw in hand, push-push-push up the hill with the wind trying to blow them all the way down again. William bent his head, Ponder bent his head, and the kite under William's arm wriggled and wriggled and tried to get free to fly away by itself. Its

tail did fly out, flap-flap-flap like a coloured streamer behind them.

At the top of the hill Ponder stood still and stared all round him.

'This – is – better – than – climbing – the – apple – tree,' he puffed. 'I really – can see – the whole – world from – here.'

There were the tiny houses down below them, tiny gardens and trees, fields and woods, stretching away to the edge of the sky. But, best of all, there was a tiny green bus winding along a grey ribbon road into the village down to the tiny piece of glass which was the pond.

'Can't see any ducks,' said Ponder.

'They're too small,' said William, and he put the kite on the grass and sat on it so that it would not wriggle away.

'Now,' he said. 'You hold the ball of string.'

'Yes,' said Ponder, and he held it firmly between his two paws.

'And every time the kite tugs at the string you must let more string off the ball,' said William.

'Yes,' said Ponder.

'But don't let go.'

'No,' said Ponder.

William stood up carefully, clutching the kite in both hands. It looked exactly like a great, fluttering red leaf with a long, long tail. Very slowly, William walked backwards away from Ponder.

'Let out some string,' he said.

'Yes,' said Ponder.

'But don't let go.'

'No,' said Ponder.

'Now!' William threw the kite up in the air. 'Oo-oo,' he shouted excitedly.

The kite whirred and wriggled and swooped and sailed up – up into the blue sky.

'It's flying, it's flying,' William cried, dancing up and down and he went chasing away after it over the Common.

Up – up went the kite, tug – tug – tug at the string. Ponder unwound the string as fast as he could. Higher and higher flew the kite, faster and faster flew the string, tug – tug – tug until the kite was only a tiny, red leaf spinning in the sky.

'DON'T LET GO!' shouted William.

'No – oo,' shouted Ponder, bouncing up and down. 'BUT THERE ISN'T ANY MORE STRING!'

Tug – tug went the kite, bounce – bounce went Ponder and then suddenly – suddenly – whoo-oo-oosh went the wind so fiercely that it lifted Ponder right off his feet. Up – up he went into the air streaming along on the end of the string.

'I'm flying,' he shouted. 'I'm flying – look at me, William – I can fly.'

William looked and there was Ponder sailing away over his head.

'Come back, Ponder,' William called. 'Come back at once.'

'I can't,' said Ponder. 'Ha, ha, this is fun. I can see more than the whole world from up here.'

'If you don't come down at once, you won't have any tea,' said William. 'And there's currant cake.'

'Is there?' said Ponder. 'Oh.'

And then – the wind stopped blowing, just like that. The kite flapped, the string flopped and Ponder felt himself falling down, down, bump!

Ponder lay on the grass with his four legs sticking straight up in the air and he laughed and laughed. William grabbed the string and started to wind it into a ball again. Very, very slowly the red leaf floated down too, giving little tugs and jerks whenever the wind came up and tried to catch it once more.

'I didn't let go,' said Ponder.

'No,' said William, 'but supposing the wind hadn't stopped. What would you have done then?'

'Flown into a tree or a fence or a telegraph pole,' said Ponder.

He sat up and shook the grass out of his fur.

'I knew I should like flying a kite,' he said. 'But I like flying myself best of all.'

Ponder's Song of the Kite

(Tune – *Over the hills and far away:*
repeat last two lines of each verse)

My kite is a leaf when it starts to fly;
A leaf with a tail,
In the windswept sky.
A kite like a leaf, a leaf with a tail,
Far up in the blue where the white clouds
    sail.

It wants to be free, my kite, in the sky,
Set free from its string,
For it longs to fly
Away by itself, away from its string,
Far up in the blue where the skylarks sing.

Ponder Makes a Cake

It was raining. Ponder and William were tired of sitting with their faces pressed to the window watching the rain going splash, splash, splash all over the garden. Even the three cats, Tigger, Ginnie, and Marmalade were tired of watching the rain and they had curled up in their baskets to go to sleep.

'The ducks on the pond like the rain, but I don't,' said William.

'The ducks on the pond like currant cake, and I do,' said Ponder. 'I wish I had a piece of currant cake, now.

'Pat-a-cake, pat-a-cake, Ponder can
Bake you a cake like the baker's man.
Biff it and bang it and mark it with P,
And put it in the oven for William and me.'

he chanted.

William stopped staring out of the window and stared at Ponder instead.

'Do you think – do you think, Ponder,' he began excitedly, 'do you think Cousin Winifred would let us make a cake for tea today – all by ourselves?'

'Currant cake?' asked Ponder, his eyes growing shiny bright.

William nodded and so, together, they slid down from the window-sill and went to find Cousin Wini-

fred. And do you know what Cousin Winifred said? She said they could make a currant cake for tea and William could take the rest of it home for his mother in the evening. But, she also said that she would light the oven for them and put everything out on the kitchen table so that they would know what they could use.

When Ponder and William went into the kitchen, there were two stools pulled up to the table; on the table was a big mixing-bowl, inside the bowl was a wooden spoon, behind the bowl was a cake-tin, and by the side of the bowl there was a row of flour, butter, salt, sugar, currants, eggs, and milk.

Ponder climbed on to his stool, seized the wooden spoon and banged the table.

'I'm ready to stir,' he said.

> 'Pat-a-cake, pat-a-cake, Ponder can
> Bake you a cake like the baker's man.
> Biff it and bang it and mark it with P,
> And put it in the oven for William and me.'

'You can't stir until I've mixed the flour and butter together,' said William.

William climbed on to his stool, tipped the flour and butter into the bowl and pounded them up with his hands. Now and again Ponder gave a helpful bang with his spoon.

'Salt,' said William, and shook the salt drum.

Ponder stirred, and the flour, butter, and salt went round and round in the bowl.

'Sugar,' said William, and shook the sugar packet.

Ponder stirred, and the flour, butter, salt, and sugar went round and round in the bowl.

'Currants,' said William.

'Currants,' said Ponder, gazing with eager eyes at the box of fat, juicy currants – a whole box full of fat, juicy currants.

'Three for you to eat now, and three for me,' said William, and he counted them out on to the table.

Ponder picked his up one by one so that they would last as long as possible. Then he stirred, and the flour, butter, salt, sugar, and currants went round and round in the bowl.

'Eggs,' said William.

He tipped two broken eggs out of a cup. Ponder stirred, but he couldn't stir quite so easily. There was

a wet, yellow patch in the middle of the bowl with all the flour, butter, salt, sugar, and currants round the edge.

'Milk,' said William and poured the milk out of a jug.

Ponder stirred, first with one paw and then with the other, but the flour, butter, salt, sugar, currants, eggs, and milk would not go round and round in the bowl. Instead, the bowl started going round and round on the table.

'Stop – stop!' shouted Ponder.

'Pat-a-cake, pat-a-cake, Ponder can,' he panted, picking the wooden spoon up in both paws and pounding it into the middle of the bowl. 'Bake you a cake like the baker's man.' Ponder stood up on his

stool. 'Biff it and bang it and mark it with P –' Ponder banged with all his might on to the wooden spoon. 'And put it in the oven for William – and – MEE –' His voice went up into a shrill squeak as the stool slipped, the bowl tipped, and Ponder went head first into the sticky cake mixture.

'Ponder!' William cried and he tried to grab the bowl, the stool, and Ponder all at once.

He pulled Ponder on to the table again and Ponder sat there with the flour, butter, salt, sugar, currants, eggs, and milk perched like a spotted hat on the top of his head. Ponder put out his tongue and licked the mixture as it slid down his nose.

'I like raw cake,' he said.

William did not say anything. He took the wooden spoon out of Ponder's paws and he scraped the raw cake off Ponder's head into the cake-tin and some of Ponder's fur went into the cake-tin as well. Then he put the cake-tin in the oven and shut the door and then – what do you think he did? He put Ponder's head under the tap in the sink, scrubbed him with the scrubbing-brush and rubbed him dry with a towel.

Ponder snorted underneath the towel.

'It's not only a currant cake,' he said. 'It's a fur cake as well.'

At tea-time Ponder and William chuckled when Cousin Winifred ate half her slice of cake and cut the other half into three pieces and gave it to the cats. She said she thought there might be something else in the cake besides flour, butter, salt, sugar, currants, eggs, and milk; and she wrapped up the rest of it for William to put in his weekend suitcase to take home.

Ponder's Song of the Cake
(Tune – *Pat-a-cake, pat-a-cake*)

Pat-a-cake, pat-a-cake,
This is the way
To bake you a cake on
A rainy day –
Butter and sugar and
Currants and flour,
Two yellow eggs and the
Milk can be sour.
Sprinkle the salt in and
Stir them about;
Beat them and pound them and
Tip them all out,
Out of the mixing-bowl
Into your tin,
Open the oven and
Push the cake in.
After an hour you may
Peep in and see
If it is ready to
Eat for your tea.

Pat-a-cake, pat-a-cake,
That is the way
To bake you a cake on
A rainy day.

Ponder and the Snow

It was deep, cold winter the weekend that William went back to stay with Cousin Winifred and Ponder, and when he woke up in the morning, his bedroom seemed to be full of light. It was a bright, white light which made the walls look brighter and whiter than they had ever done before.

William jumped out of bed and climbed on to the window-sill.

'Look, look, Ponder,' he cried. 'It's snow.'

Ponder was still half asleep and he rubbed his eyes with his paws before padding very slowly across to the window-sill.

'Snow,' he said as he looked out, too. 'What's snow?'

'That is,' said William. 'All that white stuff is snow.'

Ponder stared and blinked. There was no colour in the garden at all. It was white everywhere, the grass, the path, the bushes; even the apple tree had white along its branches.

'Oh,' said Ponder. 'Can you eat it?'

'No,' said William.

'Is it warm, like a blanket?' asked Ponder.

'No,' said William.

'What does it do?' asked Ponder.

'Nothing,' said William. 'It is cold and wet and you play with it.'

'Do you?' said Ponder. 'I don't. I'm going back to bed.' And he scampered away and hid under the eiderdown.

'When I've had my breakfast,' said William, pulling off his pyjamas, 'you are coming out in the garden with me.'

'No, I'm not,' said a gruff voice from under the eiderdown.

William washed and dressed as fast as he could and then he had to pull Ponder out from under the eiderdown and carry him downstairs to the kitchen.

William started to eat his breakfast.

'When I've eaten my porridge,' he said, 'I shall put on my boots, my coat, my scarf, my gloves, and my woolly hat and then we are going out to play.'

'Don't want to,' said Ponder.

'We are going out to play,' said William firmly.

'Won't,' said Ponder. And what do you think he did? He stamped one of his back paws hard. 'I won't. I won't.'

Have you ever wondered what you look like when you are very cross and stamp your feet and say you won't? Well, Ponder looked even crosser than that.

'You might like the snow,' said William.

'I shan't,' said Ponder.

'You don't know until you've tried. You can come out and try it with me and if you don't like it, you can come in again and watch while I make a snowman.'

William put his porridge plate on the draining-board. Then he pulled on his boots and he put on his coat, his scarf, his gloves, and his woolly hat and he took Ponder's paw.

'Want to go out of the window like the cats,' said Ponder gruffly and he climbed on to the sink.

Tigger, Ginnie, and Marmalade were all sitting on the sill and every time they put a paw down into the snow, they picked it up again and shook it. It was plain to Ponder that they didn't like the cold, wet, white stuff.

Ponder took a deep, deep, breath and he made a high, high jump right up into the air and he came down, down, down, down until he found he was sitting at the bottom of a deep, deep hole with only the tips of his black ears showing and the white stuff all round him.

Ponder lifted his paw and he hit the white stuff; he hit it again and it was all soft and crumbly. He poked his nose into it, he kicked it, he stamped on it,

he rolled on it, he bounced on it, he danced on it, he tried to swim in it until there was no black on him anywhere and he was covered in it.

'I like snow!' he shouted to William and he picked up a great pawful of snow and threw it at the cats on the window-sill.

'Ponder, that's very unkind,' said William and he ran indoors to find Cousin Winifred.

Ponder jumped through the window on to the sink. His black eyes were shiny bright.

'I like snow!' he said again, and before William could stop him he shook himself.

Whirra – whirra – whirra – whirra – and the snow flew off his fur all over the kitchen.

It went into the porridge saucepan on the gas-stove, on to the boiler and hissed, into William's slippers, and some went plop into the milk jug.

Whirra – whirra – whirra – whirra – went Ponder.

William pulled him off the sink and shut the window.

'Naughty Ponder,' he said. 'We will go out again and –'

'And make a snowman?' asked Ponder.

'Yes, and –'

'And throw snowballs?'

'Yes, but not at the cats, and –'

'And –' said Ponder.

'And,' said William, 'you must shake yourself before you come indoors next time.'

Which was a very sensible thing to say, don't you think?

And Ponder nodded his head to show that he would try to be good – whirra – whirra – whirra – whirra – and the wet drops flew all over the floor.

Ponder's Song of the Snow
(Tune – *Mary had a little lamb*)

When I go in the garden
And the snow is on the ground,
I stamp my feet
And clap my paws
And scamper round and round.
I roll upon the white stuff
Till it's sticking to my fur.
Then stand quite still
And shake myself –
A – whirra – whirra – whirr!

I like to chase the white stuff
When it whirls and flutters by;
To catch the flakes
And toss them up
As snowballs to the sky;
Or wait until I'm covered
With the snowflakes in my fur.
Then all I do
Is shake myself –
A – whirra – whirra – whirr!

Ponder and the Bird-Table

The next day while the snow was still hard and crisp on the ground, William said to Ponder – 'We ought to give the birds some food.'

'Why?' said Ponder.

'Because they might be hungry,' said William. 'All their food is under the snow and they can't find anything to eat.'

Ponder scampered away into the kitchen.

'We can feed them like we feed the ducks,' he said and held up a piece of bread in his paws.

William shook his head.

'If we put the food on the ground, Tigger, Ginnie, and Marmalade will eat it. We must put it where the cats can't see it.'

'Up very high?' said Ponder.

'Up very high,' said William.

'On top of a post?' said Ponder.

'On top of a post,' said William.

They looked out of the window down the garden and there, standing up straight in the snow, was a square, brown post. Cousin Winifred tied the sunflowers to it in the summer.

'There's a post,' said Ponder and before William had time to say any more, he had pushed open the window and jumped down into the garden.

Ponder floundered through the snow to the post and dug his claws into it.

'Look at me!' he shouted and waved his piece of bread.

William had to put on his boots, his coat, his scarf, his gloves, and his woolly hat. It took him so long that, when he ran into the garden, Ponder had already climbed to the top of the post and was sitting there still waving his piece of bread.

'The cats won't find the bread here,' he said.

'But the cats can climb, too,' said William. 'We must put a flat piece of wood on the post to make a table for the birds and then Tigger, Ginnie, and Marmalade won't be able to reach the food.'

'Flat piece of wood, flat piece of wood,' Ponder kept saying as he climbed down the post. 'I know where there is a flat piece of wood.' And he ran indoors again.

William ran after him and stood in the kitchen pulling off his boots, his coat, his scarf, his gloves, and his woolly hat while Ponder rattled about in the larder.

'There,' said Ponder, 'there's a flat piece of wood,' and he dragged it with one paw on to the kitchen floor.

'That is Cousin Winifred's pastry-board,' said William, 'and we can't use that.'

'Oh,' said Ponder, and dragged it back again.

Then he scampered into the dining-room and came out with another flat piece of wood.

'That is Cousin Winifred's best tray,' said William, 'and we can't use that.'

'Oh,' said Ponder, and dragged it back again.

Then he suddenly jumped on to the sink, squeezed through the window again, and raced through the snow to the end of the garden.

William pulled on his boots, his coat, his scarf, his gloves, and his woolly hat as fast as he could and ran after him.

'There,' said Ponder as he came out of the garden

shed. 'That's a flat piece of wood which we can use.'

And it was – it was an old seed-box.

'It will make a very good table,' said Ponder and he put it on his head to show William what he meant.

William chuckled; he chuckled and chuckled and couldn't stop.

'You do look funny, Ponder,' he said. 'It's like a great big sun hat.'

Ponder held on to the seed-box tightly and he raced round and round the garden.

'Funny Ponder, funny Ponder, I've got a sun hat,' he chanted and he galloped after the three cats, who had come out to see what all the noise was about.

Tigger, Ginnie, and Marmalade ran away and hid in the garden shed until it seemed quiet and safe again.

When Ponder was out of breath he puffed up to William and took the box off his head.

'Now, we can put it on top of the post,' he said.

William had to find a hammer, some nails, and a stool to stand on so that he could fix the box to the top of the post.

'There,' said Ponder, when it was firm and steady. 'Now we have made a bird-table and we can put the food on it.'

Cousin Winifred gave them some more bread, some pieces of bacon rind, and a saucer of water. Then William and Ponder hurried indoors, where William took off his boots, his coat, his scarf, his gloves, and his woolly hat, and they both stood at the window to watch the birds come down to the table.

But as for Tigger, Ginnie, and Marmalade, they crept out of the shed and sat in a circle at the bottom of the post, looking very cross indeed.

Ponder's Song of the Birds

One morning very early I heard the birds
   singing,
Singing while the moon was shining in the
   sky.
The garden was in darkness; nobody was
   stirring,
Nobody to hear them,
But the moon and I.

That morning very early I heard the birds
   singing,
Singing when the trees were frosted with the
   snow,
The singing was of sunlight; daffodils
   a-dancing,
Daffodils all golden
In the grass below.

Ponder and the Mouse

It was snowing too hard for Ponder and William to go into the garden in the afternoon. Cousin Winifred sat down in front of the fire with a book to read, and the three cats, Tigger, Ginnie, and Marmalade curled up in their baskets to go to sleep. Ponder and William did not want to go to sleep.

'Let's play hide-and-seek,' said William. 'I'll hide first.'

'I'll count up to ten and shout – "Coming!"' said Ponder.

William ran away and Ponder sat very still with his eyes closed, but as he couldn't see anything to count on, he had to open his eyes and say slowly – 'Tigger, Ginnie, Marmalade, Cousin Winifred, and me.' That made five and so he said it all over again to make it up to ten. 'Coming!' he shouted and scampered out of the room into the kitchen.

Ponder opened the cupboards, the larder, and the refrigerator. Then he opened all the drawers and the oven, but he couldn't see William anywhere there, so he scampered into the sitting-room.

'Coming!' he shouted.

He looked under all the chairs, in the bookcase, behind the settee, and on top of the piano, but he couldn't see William anywhere there.

'Coming!' he shouted and bounced out into the hall, past Cousin Winifred's shopping basket on wheels with the yellow waterproof cover, and up the stairs into the bathroom.

'Coming!' he shouted.

Ponder looked in the bath, in the washbasin, in the

dirty linen basket, and he stood on tiptoe to peer into the airing-cupboard and behind the hot-water tank. But he couldn't see William anywhere there.

'Coming!' he shouted and raced into Cousin Winifred's bedroom.

He crawled under the bed and out the other side; he climbed on to the bed and he pulled off the bedspread and eiderdown. Then he looked under the dressing-table and opened all the dressing-table drawers; he tugged open the wardrobe door and, as the wardrobe was so large, he had to scramble inside among Cousin Winifred's coats and dresses and the little heaps of moth-balls which made him sneeze. When he had walked round the inside of the wardrobe, he tumbled out again, climbed on a chair, and

looked on top of the wardrobe – there was plenty of dust, but no sign of William anywhere there.

'Coming!' he shouted.

Ponder jumped down and scampered along the landing to William's bedroom.

He bounced on to the bed and looked in the pillow-

cases; he looked behind the curtains and out of the window, but as it was still snowing he knew William could not be anywhere there. He looked under the bed, in the drawers, in the cupboard, in William's weekend suitcase and, last of all, he looked in the toothbrush mug on the window-sill – but William was not anywhere there. Do you know where William was hiding? If you do, you are cleverer than Ponder.

Ponder sat on the floor. He scratched his ears with one paw and he scratched them with the other. He stood up with a determined look on his face and marched down the stairs.

'Coming!' he shouted.

At the bottom of the stairs he heard a little squeak. Ponder stopped and listened – squeak – creak – and it came from Cousin Winifred's shopping basket on wheels.

'It's a mouse,' whispered Ponder. 'Whatever will Cousin Winifred say when she knows there's a mouse in her shopping basket?' And he forgot all about William.

Ponder tiptoed up to the shopping basket.

'Come out, mouse!' he shouted.

But the mouse didn't come out – it went on squeaking and creaking inside the shopping basket louder than ever.

'Ponder's not afraid of you,' Ponder said boldly. 'I'll catch you,' he said, jumping up and down. 'Out, mouse, out!' he shouted and he seized Cousin Winifred's best umbrella and rushed at the shopping basket.

The shopping basket toppled over, the waterproof cover flew off and there was – what do you think? Of

course, it was William and he was laughing so much that he could hardly stand up straight.

'I've caught *you*, Ponder, haven't I?' he laughed – and Ponder had to say 'yes' because he had never thought of looking for William anywhere there.

After that Cousin Winifred came out of the dining-room and said that if they were very quick in shutting all the drawers and cupboards that Ponder had left open, they could sit in front of the fire with her and toast crumpets for tea. Then she thought it would be time for William to go to the station to catch his train home.

Ponder's Song of Hide-and-Seek

(Tune – *I have a little pony, his name is Dapple Grey*)

I've opened all the cupboards,
Hunted in the drawers.
I've peeped inside the oven
And peered behind the doors.
I've climbed inside the wardrobe,
Crawled underneath the chairs
And shouted 'Coming! Coming!'
When running up the stairs.
There's no one in the bathroom
Nor even in the bed –
He could have moved the pillows
And hidden there instead –
I've hunted in the kitchen,
The larder and the hall.
I think the house is empty,
He's nowhere here at all.
Perhaps when he is hungry
He'll come to eat his tea.
If you know where he's hiding,
Then – you're cleverer than me!

Ponder Picks Bluebells

There was pink and white blossom on the apple tree when William came back for his weekend holiday in the spring. Cousin Winifred said she would pack a picnic basket and they would spend the day in the bluebell woods on the other side of the Common.

Paw in hand, Ponder and William set out with Cousin Winifred, over the Common where they had flown the kite, through the meadow full of yellow buttercups, and down to the edge of the bluebell wood.

When Ponder saw the bluebell wood he stood still and stared, just as he had when he first saw the sea, for he had never thought that there could be so many bluebells in the whole world.

They stretched away, up the hillside between the trees, down the slope among the little low bushes, round corners and paths, between the stones; in fact, wherever he looked there were bluebells, some in the sun, some in the shade – and the smell was the most delicious he had ever smelt.

'There,' said William, 'we may pick a bunch each, but we mustn't take too many. They look much prettier growing here and other people want to see them, too.'

Ponder did not know where to start. He wanted

to run and jump and roll in all directions at once.

'You mustn't walk on the bluebells,' said William. 'There are plenty along by the paths.' And off he went with Cousin Winifred to find a sunny place to have the picnic.

Ponder wandered away by himself. He felt happy and good and, as he walked, he picked one bluebell here, one bluebell there. But the more he looked, the

more it seemed to him that the biggest and bluest bluebells were growing farthest away inside the woods off all the paths.

Ponder turned round to see if William was watching him, but William was too busy unpacking the picnic basket near a tree to notice what Ponder was doing. Very carefully, lifting his feet high over the flowers, Ponder stepped through the bluebells to a clump that seemed to be nearly as tall as he was and he started to pick.

> 'When I go in the garden
> And the snow is on the ground,
> I stamp my feet and clap my paws
> And scamper round and round -'

he sang.

Then he stopped, for down at his feet, there was something; it wasn't a bluebell and it wasn't snow. Ponder peered through the leaves – the something was dark and covered with bristles.

'It's a prickly old scrubbing-brush,' said Ponder. 'What an untidy person to throw away a dirty old prickle-brush in the middle of a bluebell wood! I'm going to pick it up and put it in the first litter-bin I see.'

Ponder bent down and put out his paw.

'Ouch!' he shouted and hurriedly put his paw in his mouth.

It was a very prickly old scrubbing-brush and it suddenly rolled itself up into a ball.

Ponder stared; he took a step backwards; he had never seen a scrubbing-brush that moved before. He kept very still and before long the prickle-brush went straight again, just like a scrubbing-brush and, to Ponder's amazement, he saw that it had a long nose at one end and two bright, black eyes which were staring at him.

Ponder started to walk away and the prickle-brush walked after him. Ponder started to run and the prickle-brush ran, too, on little short legs which went as fast as clockwork.

Ponder fled to the path.

'Help! Help!' he shouted. 'The prickle-brush is after me!'

He looked over his shoulder and there was the prickle-brush-scrubbing-brush still chasing along making funny snorting noises as it ran.

'Help – William – help!' Ponder shouted. 'I'm being chased by a scrubbing-brush!'

Down at the bottom of the slope Ponder could see William with the picnic lunch spread round him, and Ponder was so frightened that he ran through everything, scattering sandwiches, apples, and the thermos flask in all directions, and he dashed behind the tree and poked his head out the other side.

'Is it still coming?' he whispered.

There was the prickle-brush-scrubbing-brush and there was William, rocking backwards and forwards with laughter.

'It's a hedgehog!' William said. 'Fancy running away from a hedgehog! He won't hurt you. He can smell our picnic basket and he wants something to eat.'

'Hedgehogs shouldn't hide in bluebell woods,' said Ponder gruffly.

'If you had kept to the path and not walked on the bluebells, you wouldn't have seen him and you wouldn't have been frightened,' said William.

Ponder came out from behind the tree; he put his bluebells in the shade; he sat down and he said in a small, good voice –

'I should like my dinner, now, please.'

'The prickle-brush is going to have dinner, too,' said William.

He poured some milk into a picnic saucer, he broke up a sandwich and floated it in the milk – and the

prickle-brush-scrubbing-brush-hedgehog shuffled up
to the saucer and drank every drop.

By the time Ponder and William had eaten their
sandwiches and apples and had drunk their milk out
of the thermos flask, the prickle-brush-scrubbing-
brush-hedgehog had scurried away to hide once more
deep in the shadows of the bluebell wood.

Ponder's Song of the Bluebell Wood

Wherever I looked in the bluebell wood,
There was blue like the summer seas
Stretching away down the shallow slopes
And spreading beneath the trees.

Wherever I looked in the bluebell wood,
There were shadows of apple-green,
Apple-green shadows under the leaves
Where the sun could not be seen.

Wherever I looked in the bluebell wood
And the gold of the sun broke through,
It seemed that a sea of gold-green light
Was dancing over the blue.

Ponder and the Lettuce Seeds

When Ponder and William came back from the bluebell wood, they went out into the garden to sow some lettuce seeds that William had brought from home.

William drew a line with the garden fork; he marked each end of the line with a stick and then he shook the lettuce seeds out of the packet into his hand.

'Will those little brown things turn into lettuces?' asked Ponder.

'Of course they will,' said William and he scattered the seeds along the row, and told Ponder to put some soil over them and pat them down.

Ponder felt like a real gardener as he walked up and down by the lettuce seeds, patting here, patting there until they were all hidden under the ground.

'Now we will water them,' said William, 'and that will make them grow.'

Ponder watched carefully as William marched up and down the row, too, with the watering-can, because he wanted to be the first to see the lettuces poking through the earth.

But the lettuces did not come up when William watered them, nor did they come up that evening. When Ponder went to bed he could not stop thinking about the lettuce seeds, and when he went to sleep, he dreamed about lettuce seeds all night – seeds that grew into fat, green lettuces in a row between two sticks.

Ponder woke up early the next morning.

'Lettuces!' he said and climbed out of bed on to the window-sill. The sky was pale blue, the sun was shining on the top of the apple tree – and the garden seemed to be full of birds.

'Lettuces!' said Ponder. 'They're sure to be up by now.'

He crept out of the room on the tips of his toes – stompa-stompa-stompa-stomp; down the stairs and along the hall to the kitchen. Ponder opened the kitchen door and there were the three cats, Tigger, Ginnie, and Marmalade fast asleep in their baskets.

'Wake up, cats!' said Ponder. 'We're going to look at the lettuces.'

The cats woke up, climbed out of their baskets, and followed Ponder on to the sink. Ponder opened the window and dropped down into the garden. Tigger, Ginnie, and Marmalade dropped down, too.

Up the path marched Ponder with the three cats behind him – stompa-stompa-stompa-stomp, up the steps and into the vegetable patch – stompa-stompa-stompa-stomp.

'There,' said Ponder, waving a paw towards the lettuce row. 'Look at my fat –' and he stopped – and he stared.

Tigger, Ginnie, and Marmalade stared, too, because there wasn't a sign of a fat, green lettuce anywhere. There was the row, there were the two sticks, but not one lettuce to be seen. Ponder marched angrily up the lettuce row, stompa-stompa-stompa-stomp. Had someone eaten the lettuces? No, there were only

his own footsteps and William's where they had gone up and down with the watering-can.

Suddenly Ponder knew – William had put the lettuce seeds in upside-down!

'Cats,' said Ponder, 'we must dig them up again.' And he raced away to find the garden fork.

Tigger, Ginnie, and Marmalade looked at each other in surprise and great, pleased smiles spread all over their faces. Never before had anyone told them they could dig in the vegetable garden. Cousin Winifred always shooed them away if they so much as put a paw near one of her cabbage plants. So, with miaows and 'prrps' of delight they bounded on to the lettuce row and three pairs of paws began to dig. Ponder hurried back with the garden fork.

'Those – lettuces –' he panted, 'have gone a long way since last night. I can't even see one tiny leaf.'

Ponder dug; Tigger dug; Ginnie and Marmalade dug; the fork and the three pairs of paws dug faster and faster and deeper and deeper.

'Ponder! What are you doing?' a voice shouted.

Ponder looked up and found that he had dug so deeply that he could only just see over the top of the hole and there, on the path, was William dancing up and down in his pyjamas.

'Tigger, Ginnie, Marmalade!' William shouted.

Tigger's surprised face peered over the rim of his hole; Ginnie's little black ears twitched above her hole and Marmalade – Marmalade was much too busy to look up and see what was happening; only the tip of his orange tail was waving out of his hole.

Ponder wiped his muddy paws on the black band across his chest and smiled at William.

'We're digging up the lettuce seeds because you put them in upside-down and instead of coming up this morning they've grown right down to the other side of the world,' he puffed, all in one breath.

William jumped on to the vegetable patch.

'Come out, come out, all of you,' he said. He seized Ponder and he shooed the cats out of their holes. 'It doesn't matter which way up you sow lettuce seeds and they haven't gone to the other side of the world because they won't start growing for weeks yet.'

He picked up the fork and began pushing back the earth. Ponder and the three cats stood and watched him.

'Shall we have to sow some more lettuce seeds?' asked Ponder.

'Yes,' said William, 'when I'm dressed and have had my breakfast.'

Ponder's black eyes were shiny bright.

'I like gardening,' he said. 'But I like the digging part best of all. Don't you, cats?'

And he marched up the garden path to the kitchen, stompa-stompa-stompa-stomp, with William, Tigger, Ginnie, and Marmalade close behind him.

Ponder's Song of the Vegetable Garden

(Tune – 'Will you walk into my parlour?'
said the spider to the fly)

If it's cabbages you're wanting,
Or a carrot or a bean,
Or a fat and juicy marrow
Striped with yellow and with green;
If it's lettuces or beetroot,
Or potatoes by the pound,
Or an onion or a parsnip –
There are plenty in the ground;
If it's turnip tops or parsley,
Pods of peas and spinach, too,
I will dig them up or pick them
Just as proper gardeners do.

Ponder and the Garden Seat

After breakfast when the fresh row of lettuce seeds had been sown, Ponder looked round the tidy vegetable patch and said –

'I know what I should like to do now.'

'Yes?' asked William.

'Paint the garden seat,' said Ponder.

William stared at the garden seat which was standing under the apple tree. There it had been all through the windy autumn and the cold, snowy winter and, in the spring sunshine, it was very shabby indeed.

Ponder's black eyes were shiny bright.

'If we paint it now, it will be ready for when you come back in the summer,' he said.

'We'd have to ask Cousin Winifred first,' said William. 'And if you had a paint brush you might get paint all over your paws.'

'No, I wouldn't,' said Ponder, shaking his head.

'You might want to stir the paint pot and then you might fall in like you did with the cake mixture.'

'No, I wouldn't,' said Ponder, shaking his head.

'You might trip over the paint pot and spill all the paint.'

'No, I wouldn't,' said Ponder, shaking his head.

William wanted to paint the garden seat, too, and so he ran indoors. When he came back again he was carrying a newspaper, which he spread under the apple tree; two brushes, one of which he gave to Ponder; a jam-jar full of green paint; a piece of clean rag and a bottle of something which Cousin Winifred had said would rub paint off dirty fingers and paws. The bottle had the letters TURPS on it, which William said stood for The Useful Remover of Paint Stains.

Ponder and William pulled the garden seat on to the newspaper. Ponder sat on the grass behind, William sat in front; they put the jam-jar between them and then they began to paint. Ponder held his brush

carefully. He did not dip it too deeply into the jam-jar and he scraped it on the side so that the paint did not run down the handle on to his paws. Slowly the garden seat changed from a shabby, dull one into a fresh green one until there were only the legs left to do, but the jam-jar of paint was empty.

'I'll ask Cousin Winifred for some more,' said William. He put his brush on the newspaper, picked up the jar, and ran indoors.

Ponder put his brush on the newspaper, too, and looked at his paws. There wasn't a speck of paint anywhere and he felt very pleased with himself. Then he

looked at the pink and white blossom on the apple tree. Then he walked down to the vegetable patch, where the lettuce seeds had been sown. Then he walked all round the vegetable patch, back up the path to the garden seat, and then – he sat down.

William came hurrying along with the jam-jar full of green paint in his hand and he stopped, quite still, when he saw Ponder.

'Ponder – you're sitting on the seat!' he exclaimed.

'Seats are meant to be sat on,' said Ponder happily.

'But it's – WET!' William shouted.

Ponder sprang into the air. The seat gave a little jump after him and there were puffs of white fur all over its fresh green surface.

'Ponder – look at your back!' squealed William. 'It's striped – like a zebra!'

Ponder spun round and round trying to see his back.

'I'm a zebra-panda,' he chanted. 'I'm a green-striped-black-and-white-zebranda and –'

'Stand still, Ponder, stand still!' William cried.

He picked up the rag and The Useful Remover of Paint Stains bottle and he caught hold of Ponder and he tried to rub him clean.

William rubbed and rubbed and rubbed, and Ponder kept trying to see behind him to find out what his back really looked like. In the end, it was a pretty pale green all over, except on Ponder's black band.

'You'll have to have a bath,' said William, 'or else you'll never be a black and white panda again – and you wouldn't like that, would you?'

'No, I wouldn't,' said Ponder, shaking his head. 'But we must paint the rest of the seat this afternoon.'

Ponder picked up the paint brushes; William took

the rag and the empty bottle of The Useful Remover of Paint Stains and together they went up the path to the house.

And the garden seat with the puffs of white fur was left under the apple tree, nearly ready for when William should come back again for another weekend holiday.

Ponder's Song of the Zebranda

(Tune – *John Brown's Body*;
Chorus – repeating last line of each verse)

Have you seen the wild zebranda marching
  round the apple tree?
His coat is smooth and shining like the
  ripples of the sea;
His eyes are large as saucers and as black as
  black can be;
The green-striped-black-and-white-
  zebranda.

Have you heard the wild zebranda purring
  gruffly in the grass?
He loves to watch the beetles and the
  grasshoppers which pass

Among the scattered dewdrops there, all
   glittering like glass;
The green-striped-black-and-white-
   zebranda.

If you greet the wild zebranda in the garden,
   he is sure
To say he's pleased to meet you and hold out
   his stubby paw,
And ask if you have ever seen the like of him
   before -
A green-striped-black-and-white-zebranda?

When you tell the wild zebranda it is time
   to say good-bye
To cats and ducks and bluebell woods, to
   boats, and kites that fly,
He'll know you're coming back again – and
   wink one gleaming eye;
The green-striped-black-and-white-zebranda.

About the author

Barbara Softly was born at Ewell in Surrey and she still
lives near there.

She took the Froebel training course and then specialized
in History and English, and has had experience of children
of all ages in her eleven years of teaching.
She likes gardening, animals, and music, and attempts to
play the clavichord. Her spare time is spent in keeping
the three cats Tigger, Ginnie and Marmalade out of the
goldfish pond and off her husband's flower beds.

Barbara Softly has written three historical novels for
boys and girls, as well as non-fiction, short stories, and articles.
Ponder and William on Holiday and *Ponder and William at Home*
are also available in Young Puffins.

*If you have enjoyed this book perhaps you will be interested to
know that over 1,000 species of animals are in danger of becoming
extinct – 'as dead as the dodo'. This is why the World Wildlife
Fund has been formed, as a kind of modern international Noah's ark
through which all animal lovers can help to save the world's wildlife
and wild places. There is a youth service of the World Wildlife
Fund and if you would like to know about it please send for
literature to:*

WORLD WILDLIFE FUND
7/8 PLUM TREE COURT
LONDON EC4

WHO IS HE?

His name is Smudge, and he's the mascot of the Junior Puffin Club.

WHAT IS THAT?

It's a Club for children between 4 and 8 who are beginning to discover and enjoy books for themselves.

HOW DOES IT WORK?

On joining, members are sent a Club badge and Membership Card, a sheet of stickers, and their first copy of the magazine, *The Egg*, which is sent to them four times a year. As well as stories, pictures, puzzles and things to make, there are competitions to enter and, of course, news about new Puffins.

For details of cost and an application form, send a stamped addressed envelope to:

The Junior Puffin Club
Penguin Books Ltd
Bath Road
Harmondsworth
Middlesex UB7 ODA